A L I E N S ™

publisher **Mike Richardson**

series editor **Barbara Kesel**
collection editor **Lynn Adair**
collection designer **Amy Arendts**

special thanks to **Maury McIntyre at Twentieth Century
Fox + Steve Perry + Kelley Jones + Den Beauvais +
Cara Niece + Rich Powers** and **Monty Sheldon**

inspired by **the original Alien designs of H.R. Giger**

Published by
Titan Books Ltd.
42-44 Dolben Street
London SE1 0UP

First edition: February 1998
ISBN: 1-85286-838-4

1 2 3 4 5 6 7 8 9 10

Printed in Canada

ALIENS™

HARVEST

script **Jerry Prosser**

pencils + inks **Kelley Jones**

colors **Les Dorscheid**

cover **John Bolton**

lettering **Clem Robins**

Titan Books

A World of People Where Monsters Lurked

It's a miracle to me that I ever drew *Aliens: Hive*, now *Harvest*.

A miracle because of the trauma I endured when I saw the original movie in 1979. I went expecting a feel-good, *Star Wars* kind of thing. Instead, I found a real horror movie. I like horror movies. I really do. I have even seen such obscure classics as *Grave of the Vampire*. How many people can say that? But *Alien*, to quote a cliché, was a real roller coaster and I hate roller coasters. They make me vomit. *Alien* very nearly made me vomit. I hate vomiting just a little more than I hate roller coasters. I loved *Alien*, though. How's that for a psychological profile?

I remember sitting next to this college football lineman when I saw the film. He brought his girlfriend. He was very tough sounding. Kind of frat. He kept telling her he'd protect her. He blubbered louder than anyone in the theater, and we were all pretty jumpy. I remember his girlfriend kept patting his shoulder and telling him it was just a movie. I was actually mildly comforted by her stalwart reassurances.

It was dark by the time the film ended. When we got to my car, my friend and I actually looked under the car and in the back seat before we got in, for fear of a giant bug-like monster with a double set of jaws lying in wait. This was before the days of *Nick at Night*, so there wasn't any kind of warm, fuzzy diversion to get your mind off your terror like there is now. You just had to lie in bed and try not to think about it.

What a primal film! I never wanted to see it again. My phobia of this film rivaled my fear of math. I tried to watch it a couple of times over the next ten years. A sort of associative therapy. I always stopped the film about 15 to 20 minutes into it. I never actually told anyone about this. I always found some excuse for backing out of a midnight film fest anytime *Alien* was included in the lineup. I usually used nausea as the excuse.

So, I had this incredible phobia no one knew about. And Barbara Kesel called me and said, "Do you want to do an *Aliens* miniseries?'

"Uh, what's it about?" I stammered back.

She told me she had two different stories in her possession and asked me to review them both and decide which one I wanted. She hung up, and I sat there thinking of excuses to get out of it. I didn't think she'd buy vomiting, considering I'd have to be sick for about the next three months. I thought of other excuses: prior deadlines, religious ceremonies, my mom wouldn't let me.

The plots arrived a few days later, and I let them sit on my coffee table for a while. I found lots of other things to do in the meantime. But I knew Barbara would be calling sooner or later, so I sat down and read the first script. It wasn't really my cup of tea — to borrow another cliché — but I was relieved. I read the second script. I looked for any little nit-picky reason why I couldn't accept. I didn't find one. The script was fantastic!

I remember being impressed with the depth of the characterization. Certainly not your usual comics fair. I found myself actually caring about what happened to these characters and wondering how the story would turn out. I had drawn a lot of stories at that point, and had read a great deal more, yet I had no idea where the plot was going or how it would end. That is such a rare thing!

Midway through the script, I flipped to the back page to see who wrote it. I expected a big-name writer, considering the quality of the story. It said "by Jerry Prosser." Who's Jerry Prosser? I wondered. I was really impressed. Here was a story that totally captured the atmosphere of the first *Alien* movie. A world of people where monsters lurked instead of the other way around.

Jerry's story is filled with a whole range of human emotion: love, envy, jealousy, greed, hope, and fear. Debilitating fear. This is really epitomized in the character Stan. Jerry's youth belies his ability to write the elderly professor so sad and alone. His masterful handling of the Aliens themselves really impressed me. This book, and Jerry's idea, came out long before the *Jurassic Park* view of monsters that do what they do, neither good nor evil, but monstrously terrifying nonetheless. I guess that pretty much cinched it for me. I had to draw this book.

When Barbara finally called, I said, "YES" before she could ask.

I've always felt good about the art in this job. Les Dorscheid's wonderful color schemes are as much a part of this series' success as Jerry's story or my pictures. Notice the natural lighting in outdoor scenes and the artificial quality of the light inside the space ships. Masterful.

So now I can watch the *Alien* movie again. Even late at night, as long as my girlfriend sits up with me. She doesn't hold my hand or anything, but she does bring me coffee. I even own the special-edition laser disc with the extra monster footage tacked to the end. And I owe it to Jerry Prosser. You could say Jerry cured me of my Alien phobia.

Now, if he could only do something about my math anxiety . . .

Kelley Jones
Citrus Heights, CA
1997

Dave Dorman's *Aliens: Hive* trade-paperback cover.

ALIENS™

SHE WAS USED TO THE DARK. IT HELD NO SURPRISES.

RIPPLES OF DARKNESS PUSHED AGAINST HER, INVISIBLE STONES DROPPED INTO A POOL OF INK.

SHE WASN'T ALONE.

SILENCE, COMPANION TO DARKNESS, WAS NOT HER FRIEND.

SHE FELT AROUND HER THE EMPTINESS OF THE VACUUM...THE GRAVE.

SHE FOUND HERSELF WHISPERING TO FILL THE SILENCE.

WHERE ARE YOU? WHERE ARE YOU?

SHE COULD NEITHER SEE NOR HEAR IT, BUT SHE COULD FEEL ITS PRESENCE.

HERE?

SHIT! BLIND ALLEY.

BACKTRACK.

HE FEELS THE IPPLES IN THE ACKNESS LAP GAINST HER, AS S MOTION STIRS THE PRISTINE STILLNESS.

SHE WONDERS HOW IT CAN MOVE SO QUICKLY.

C'MON ...LET'S GO.

OOH, I HATE THIS PART...

PRIORITY OVERRIDE. CODE MYRMIDON.

CANCEL PREDATION FUNCTIONS. RETURN TO STANDARD PROGRAM.

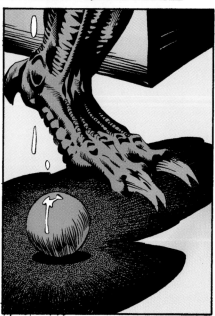

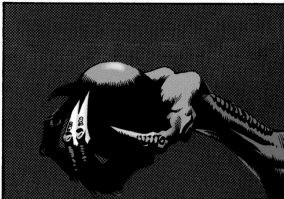

WOOF WOOF ARF

REPORT TO THE LAB AT 15:30. I WANT TO DOWNLOAD AND REVIEW.

AND KEEP MAC QUIET. THE CREW IS STILL IN HYPERSLEEP.

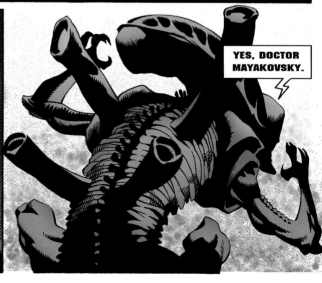

YES, DOCTOR MAYAKOVSKY.

DID YOU ENJOY THE SHOW, *ARI?*

SYMPTOMS SEEM TO BE COMING CLOSER TOGETHER.

SO LITTLE LEFT. SO LITTLE TIME.

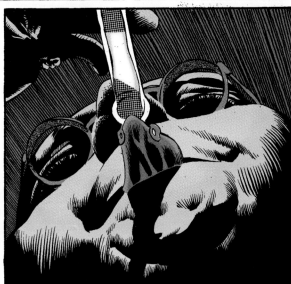

THE MEMORIES BEGIN WITH A WARM TINGLE AT THE BACK OF HIS NECK. THE WARMTH SPREADS QUICKLY THROUGH BOTH HIS BODY AND PSYCHE.

HE FLIPS THROUGH HIS MEMORIES LIKE THE PAGES OF A WELL-WORN BOOK UNTIL HE FINDS WHAT HE'S LOOKING FOR.

AS TIME...TURNS...BLUE...

HOW DO YOU KNOW ALL THIS ABOUT ME?

I LIKE TO KNOW EVERYTHING I CAN ABOUT *MY PARTNERS.*

"I KNOW YOU DON'T LIKE THOSE PEOPLE...THE ONES YOU'RE FORCED TO DEAL WITH.

"I KNOW YOU'RE RUNNING OUT OF MONEY...AND TIME."

HE REMEMBERS EVERYTHING ABOUT THAT NIGHT...HER EYES, HER SMILE, THE WAY HE FELT AND THE PLAN. IT SEEMS TO BE HAPPENING ALL OVER AGAIN...AND AGAIN...

HE TOUCHES ON EACH FROZEN MOMENT WITH HER AND HOLDS IT. THE SUBLIME PERFECTION OF MEMORY.

THE BEST PLACE TO GET HONEY IS FROM BEES.

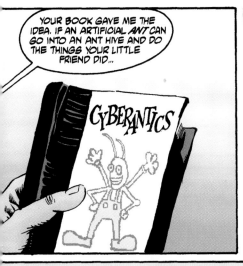

YOUR BOOK GAVE ME THE IDEA. IF AN ARTIFICIAL *ANT* CAN GO INTO AN ANT HIVE AND DO THE THINGS YOUR LITTLE FRIEND DID...

CYBERANTICS

WHY CAN'T AN ARTIFICIAL ALIEN PENETRATE THEIR SOCIETY?

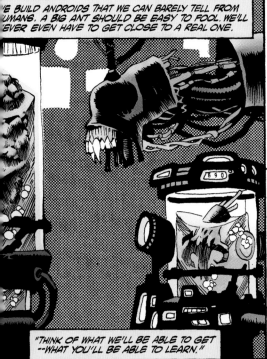

'E BUILD ANDROIDS THAT WE CAN BARELY TELL FROM UMANS. A BIG ANT SHOULD BE EASY TO FOOL. WE'LL EVER EVEN HAVE TO GET CLOSE TO A REAL ONE.

"THINK OF WHAT WE'LL BE ABLE TO GET --WHAT YOU'LL BE ABLE TO LEARN."

I'VE BEEN A THIEF FOR A LONG TIME, STAN. I KNOW WHEN TO TAKE A RISK. THIS IS IT.

I WAS ABLE TO *CONVINCE* A BIO-NATIONAL EXECUTIVE NOT TO TAKE CERTAIN SECRETS TO HIS GRAVE. I KNOW WHERE IT IS, STAN...A MOUNTAIN OF GOLD!

WE'VE REACHED ORBIT AROUND A PLANET MARKED ON THE CHARTS AS *A6 454*. IT'S SO FAR OFF THE USUAL ROUTES THAT IT HASN'T EVEN HAD A FORMAL SURVEY.

HOWEVER, FROM THE READINGS WE'VE GATHERED, WE KNOW THAT THIS PLANET DOES HAVE A BARELY BREATHABLE ATMOS-PHERE, AND SEEMS TO BE CONSTANTLY BUFFETED BY STORMS.

WE ALSO KNOW THERE IS MATERIAL OF GREAT VALUE ON THE PLANET, THE NATURE OF THIS MATERIAL IS NEED-TO-KNOW ONLY.

WHO NEEDS TO KNOW?

THE CAPTAIN ALREADY KNOWS --THAT'S WHY WE'RE HERE. THE MEMBERS OF THE MISSION CREW WILL ALSO BE BRIEFED.

I'LL ALSO BE LOOKING FOR VOLUNTEERS TO--

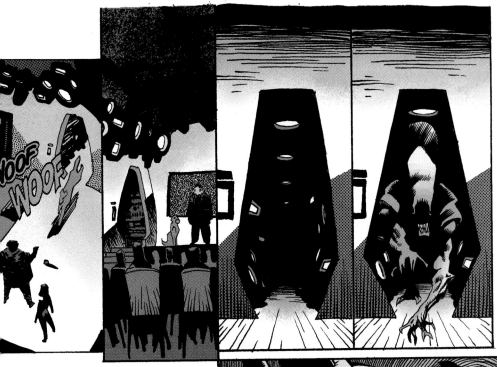

DON'T MOVE! HE WON'T ATTACK UNLESS...

...PROVOKED!

NUH NUH NUH

PRIORITY OVERRIDE! CODE MYRMIDON!

"HOBAN, THIS IS LISH. WE'VE CLEARED THE BAY AND ARE ON AN APPROACH VECTOR TO THE SURFACE.

"PLANET HAS A HEAVY RADIATION BELT--NO TIME FOR SIGHTSEEING.

"GILL, KEEP YOUR EYES ON THE HULL IONIZATION.

"YOU DON'T LOOK VERY GOOD, STAN.

" HOBAN, WE'RE ON OUR FINAL APPROACH."

SEE? WHAT DID I TELL YOU, STAN? A WALK IN THE PARK.

GGGGGGGGGGGG

CONTACT WITH ATMOSPHERE ...NOW.

SSSSSSSSS

ANYTHING LEFT?

DOLOMITE'S LOG. CAPTAIN'S ENTRY. FOLLOWING THE LAUNCH OF THE MISSION PLATFORM, I'VE DECIDED TO EXAMINE SOME OF THE DEBRIS WE NOTICED IN ORBIT. UNDER CLOSER SCRUTINY, WE'VE DISCOVERED THE REMAINS OF A SHIP.

TWO MEN HAVE GONE ON BOARD TO LOOK FOR ONE OF THE SHIP'S **BLACK BOXES.** I HOPE TO FIND OUT WHAT HAPPENED AND IF IT WILL AFFECT OUR MISSION.

WE'RE GETTING CLOSE. I'VE GOT IT ON A LOCATOR. IT'S JUST THAT...WHAT IF ONE OF THOSE THINGS...?

TAKE IT EASY. DON'T GET SPOOKED.

I'VE GOT THE RECORDER.

GET THAT THING BACK HERE ON THE DOUBLE! I WANT TO KNOW WHAT HAPPENED TO THAT SHIP.

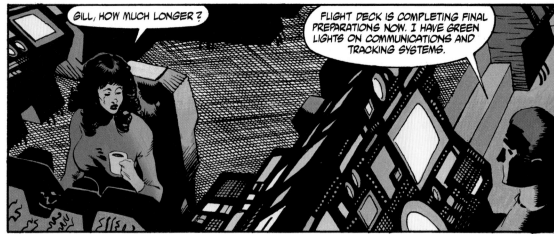

GILL, HOW MUCH LONGER?

FLIGHT DECK IS COMPLETING FINAL PREPARATIONS NOW. I HAVE GREEN LIGHTS ON COMMUNICATIONS AND TRACKING SYSTEMS.

STAN'LL WANT TO GO OVER SOME LAST-MINUTE DETAILS, I'M SURE.

WILL YOU LOOK AT THE SIZE OF THIS THING...

THE HIVE IS ALMOST 1000 METERS HIGH. PRETTY IMPRESSIVE ON A PLANET WHERE THE HIGHEST NATURALLY-OCCURRING "PEAK" IS ONLY 350 METERS.

THE WEATHER IS OBSCURING THE IMAGING SYSTEM. I HOPE NORBERT DOESN'T HAVE ANY TROUBLE.

YOU NEVER KNOW WHAT ELSE MIGHT BE DOWN THERE.

WHAT DO YOU WANT?

SORRY, NO TIME. MAYBE YOU CAN GET NORBERT TO PLAY WITH YOU BEFORE YOU LEAVE.

WHAT DO YOU THINK OF ALL THIS?

WHY DO YOU ASK?

WELL... I GUESS YOU HAVE A UNIQUE PERSPECTIVE.

I'D ASK NORBERT, BUT HE DOESN'T HAVE VERBAL PROGRAMMING AS SOPHISTICATED AS YOURS. BESIDES, HE GIVES ME THE CREEPS.

I FEEL LIKE ANY OTHER MEMBER OF THE CREW. I HAVE A JOB. I DO IT.

MAY I SEE YOUR HANDS?

DON'T YOU FIND HUMAN ENDEAVOR-- LIKE THIS MISSION --INTERESTING?

NOT PARTICULARLY. I FIND MOST HUMANS QUITE BORING.

THEY LOOK SO MUCH LIKE MY FATHER'S HANDS. I'D BETTER GO GET STAN. I HOPE WE GET THE CHANCE TO TALK SOME MORE.

ONE LAST THING...

YES?

SOMETIMES I THINK IT WOULD BE BETTER TO BE A SYNTHETIC, ABLE TO RE-PROGRAM MYSELF WITH A NEW CHIP OR BIO-ELECTRICAL CIRCUIT.

DO YOU EVER THINK YOU'RE MISSING SOME-THING? BY NOT BEING HUMAN, I MEAN?

NOT THAT I'M AWARE OF.

I'M GOING TO GET STAN. SEE YOU SOON.

GILL? HOBAN HERE. I HAVE SOME INFORMATION FOR YOU. ARE STAN OR JULIE THERE?

NO.

THE DEBRIS WE ENCOUNTERED IN ORBIT *WAS* A WRECKED SHIP. WE MANAGED TO GET A FLIGHT RECORDER. I'LL PUT THE LAST OF IT THROUGH TO YOU.

THIS IS *CAPTAIN POTTER* OF *THE LANCET.*

YOU ARE GUILTY OF CRIMINAL TRESPASS. YOU WON'T LIVE TO REGRET YOUR DECISION.

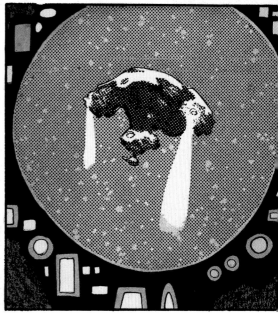

COMPUTER OFF LINE AT 15:30:42 _____

MY GUESS IS THAT THEY'RE STILL SOMEWHERE IN TH SECTOR. SAVE THIS INFORMATION UNDER SECURE FIL HJ 3729. YOU WILL MAKE NO MENTION OF THIS TO ANY OTHER CREWMEMBER.

DO YOU UNDER-STAND?

YES.

SHE ENTERS THE SOFT LIGHT OF THE ROOM.

BY THE LOOK ON HIS FACE, SHE CAN TELL HE IS OUTSIDE OF TIME. A SOLITARY IMMORTAL MADE OF WAX.

SHE MUSES ON THE VALUE OF AN ETERNITY CONSISTING ONLY OF SOLIPSISM AND MEMORY.

HOW MUCH TIME DO THEY HAVE LEFT?

CAN SHE EVEN THINK IN SUCH TERMS, AS HE MOVES IN FROZEN TIME -- LIKE THE RUNNER IN ZENO'S FIRST PARADOX ? THE FINISH LINE DRAWS CLOSER, YET NO CLOSER, THROUGH AN INFINITE SERIES OF DIVISIONS OF THE DISTANCE.

HOW CAN THE RACE END WHEN IT'S IMPOSSIBLE TO BEGIN?

STAN ? WHAT ARE YOU DREAMING ABOUT? AM I WITH YOU ?

WHAT...

HOW LONG HAVE I BEEN OUT?

NOT LONG. WE'RE JUST NOW GETTING READY.

I WAS DREAMING OF YOU. WE WERE...

SSHHH. I'D RATHER HAVE YOUR TRAVELS BE SECRETS. THAT WAY YOU'RE SO MUCH MORE *MYSTERIOUS*.

THE ONLY MYSTERY ABOUT ME IS HOW LONG IT WILL BE UNTIL I START BELIEVING THAT KIND OF TALK FROM YOU.

JULIE, I...I'D LIKE TO ASK YOU A *FAVOR*.

YES?

IF YOU'RE MAKING ANY OF THIS UP FOR MY BENEFIT...

PLEASE DON'T STOP.

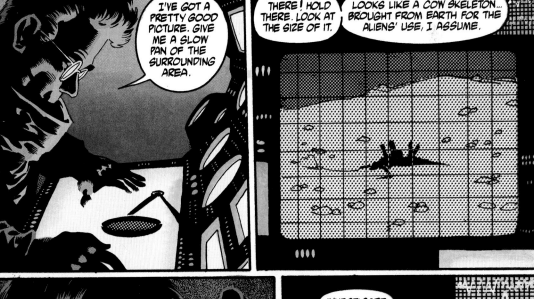

...LIE, PLEASE TAKE GILL OUT OF THE ...OOM. HIS BEHAVIORAL PROGRAMMING MAY ...VE HIM AN EMBOLISM IF HE OBSERVES ANY MORE.

HE MAY BE COMPELLED TO ACT. I WOULDN'T WANT HIM TO DO ANYTHING *FOOLISH*.

GILL, SOME-DAY YOU AND I MUST HAVE A LITTLE *TALK* ABOUT YOUR PROGRAM-MING. IT SHOULD MAKE YOU A LITTLE LESS *PREDICTABLE*.

XL1, GIVE ME A GOOD PICTURE OF THE LOCKING MECHANISM ON THE DOOR.

THAT'S PRETTY STANDARD. SHOULDN'T BE TOO MUCH TROUBLE. XL1, RIP OUT THE KEY PAD AND TURN THE HANDLE MANUALLY.

WHAT IS HE DOING *AWAKE*?

HOW THE HELL SHOULD I KNOW?

HOW SOON TO THE RENDEZVOUS? WITH *LANCET*?

SOON ...OUGH.

FIRE!

AAAAAIEEEE

SKRRAAAK

PLEASE CLEAR YOUR VISUAL RECEPTORS AND TAKE A SLOW SCAN OF THE AREA.

THAT'S BETTER. *MUCH* BETTER.

T LOOKS LIKE THE BEEKEEPERS HAVE BEEN HERE BEFORE US.

LET'S JUST GET SOMEBODY DOWN THERE TO PILOT THE THING --WE'LL BOTH GO BACK TO *THE DOLOMITE.*

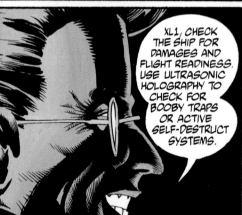

XL1, CHECK THE SHIP FOR DAMAGES AND FLIGHT READINESS. USE ULTRASONIC HOLOGRAPHY TO CHECK FOR BOOBY TRAPS OR ACTIVE SELF-DESTRUCT SYSTEMS.

THIS SYSTEM APPEARS TO BE SERIOUSLY DAMAGED. I CANNOT DETERMINE ITS FUNCTION.

GIVE ME A VISUAL OF CONDITIONS OUTSIDE.

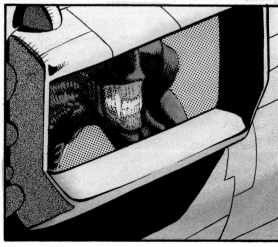

WELL, NOW WE KNOW WHAT IT DID. IT LOOKS LIKE THE CREW WAS USING SOME SORT OF INFRASONIC SUPPRESSION SYSTEM...

INGENIOUS. THEY USED IT THE SAME WAY A BEEKEEPER USES SMOKE. I WISH I WOULD HAVE THOUGHT OF IT.

WE MIGHT AS WELL TEST THE REST OF OUR EQUIPMENT. TAKE MAC OUTSIDE.

SORRY, BOY.

EEP CLOSE TABS N THEM. SINCE OUR ORK'S BEEN DONE OR US, WE'VE GOT SOME TIME FOR *RESEARCH.*

ACTIVATE YOUR TRACKING SYSTEM. I WANT A TRAIL LEFT THAT WE CAN FOLLOW LATER.

Ari could not see far into the forest of grass that reached high into the sky. She activated her sense of smell and a whole new world presented itself: a world filled with subtle variation, its complex structure based upon molecular chemistry rather than sound or light. *

She tested the air for signs of pheromones left by the other ants. There it was. A trail.

Ari followed the trail until she reached a nest of ants.

She stood and watched them for some time. They moved in and out of the hive with such determination and precision.

What a commotion!

Ants came into the clearing carrying food. Others rushed to assist them with their burdens.

m CYBERANTICS by Stanislaw Mayakovsky.

The hive was filled with activity.

Others were attending to the eggs and larvae.

Ari could hear all the ants moving around her. Some were carrying food to storage areas.

Ari could hear the incessant clickings of the young ants. "Food. Food. Food..."

She followed the sound to proceed with the next phase of her program.

The center of life in the hive --

-- the Queen.

THERE'S THE GRAND OLD LADY HERSELF.

XL1, ADVANCE AND ACTIVATE RECOGNITION PROGRAMMING.

Ari understood that her next action was to enter the nest.

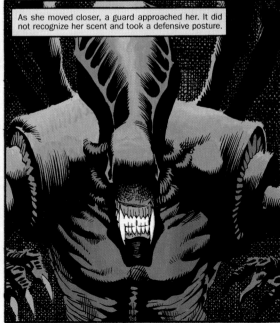

As she moved closer, a guard approached her. It did not recognize her scent and took a defensive posture.

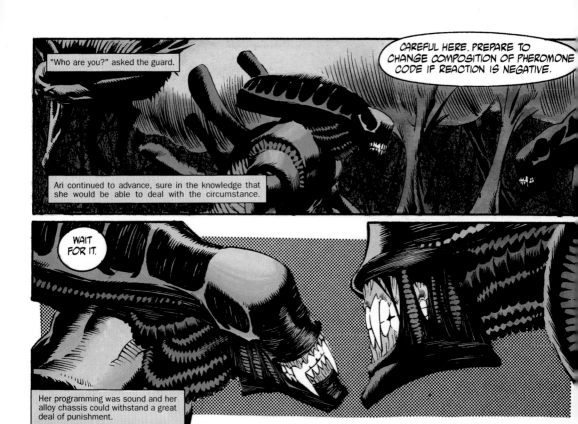

"Who are you?" asked the guard.

CAREFUL HERE. PREPARE TO CHANGE COMPOSITION OF PHEROMONE CODE IF REACTION IS NEGATIVE.

Ari continued to advance, sure in the knowledge that she would be able to deal with the circumstance.

WAIT FOR IT.

Her programming was sound and her alloy chassis could withstand a great deal of punishment.

WAIT FOR...

SHIT! GO! GET OUT OF THERE!

ALL SYSTEMS ON LINE! DEFENSE MODE ALPHA!

Ari ran through the nest as fast as her six legs could carry her.

The wave of the glistening black bodies moved ahead with the precision of a military regime on the parade grounds. A million-legged phalanx.

The desire to reach their destination coursed through black, chitinous bodies.

Mandibles snapped and ground in anticipation.

NO.

NO!

DAMN! WHY THE HELL DID I SEND HIM INSIDE? WE HAD EVERYTHING WE CAME FOR.

GILL, DO YOU COPY? THIS IS HOBAN.

I'M RECEIVING YOU, SIR, BUT THE SIGNAL IS WEAK.

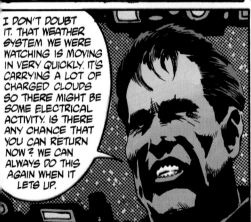

I DON'T DOUBT IT. THAT WEATHER SYSTEM WE WERE WATCHING IS MOVING IN VERY QUICKLY. IT'S CARRYING A LOT OF CHARGED CLOUDS SO THERE MIGHT BE SOME ELECTRICAL ACTIVITY. IS THERE ANY CHANCE THAT YOU CAN RETURN NOW? WE CAN ALWAYS DO THIS AGAIN WHEN IT LETS UP.

THAT SHOULDN'T BE NECESSARY. WE ALREADY HAVE A FULL CARGO HOLD OF JELLY.

HOW?

WE WERE LUCKY ENOUGH TO HAVE RUN INTO SOME BEEKEEPERS, BUT THE CYBERNETIC ALIEN WAS DESTROYED.

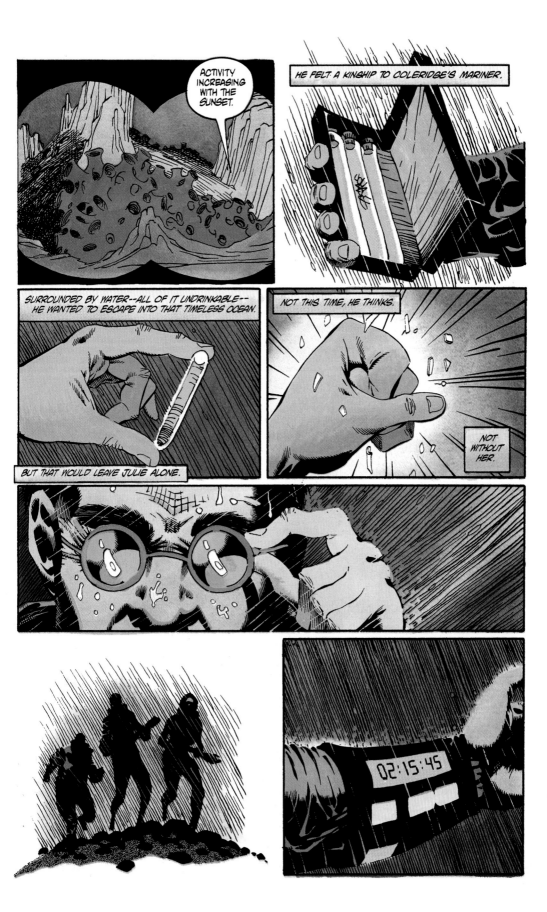

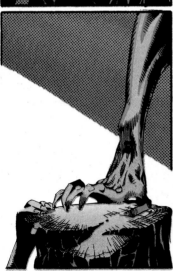

SHE STOPS BREATHING, SLIPPING INTO PRACTICED SILENCE.

IT'S NO WORSE THAN ANY OTHER JOB, SHE THINKS TO HERSELF.

SHE WELCOMES HER FRIEND, THE DARKNESS, BUT THE SILENCE HERE UNNERVES HER.

SHE TAKES SOME COMFORT IN HEARING STAN'S LABORED BREATHING, BUT PRAYS IT IS NOT TOO CONSPICUOUS.

A SCHOLARLY LIFESTYLE DIDN'T GIVE HIM MUCH PREPARATION FOR THIS.

SHE HAS NO DOUBTS ABOUT GILL'S FUNCTIONING, BUT STAN IS ANOTHER MATTER.

SHE WONDERS WHY SHE IS DRAWN TO HIM. HIS QUEST FOR A SOLITARY IMMORTALITY PUZZLES HER.

HIS SOJOURNS AWAY FROM HER, AWAY FROM TIME, LEAVE HER UPSET AND LONELY. HIS DEPARTURE LEAVES A VACUUM THAT TOO SUDDENLY SNAPS CLOSED.

WHAT IS LEFT FOR HER BESIDES THE MEMORY OF HIS PASSING...

...AND EMPTINESS?

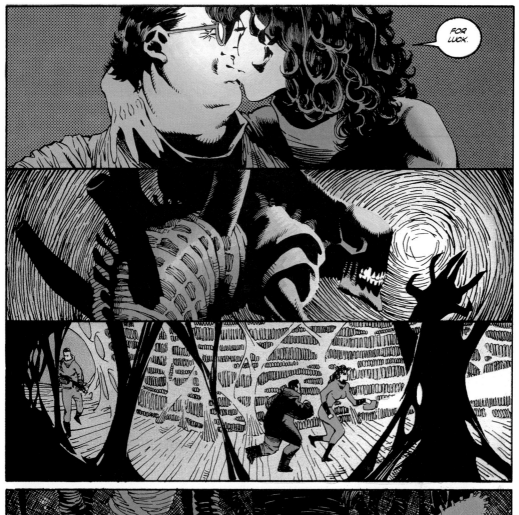

IT FLOWS
OUT OF THE
DARKNESS.

SHE CURSES ITS
DEADLY SILENCE.

THE CREATURE SENSES SOME-
THING NOT USUALLY FOUND IN
THIS LEVEL OF THE NEST, BUT
CANNOT DETERMINE THE SOURCE.

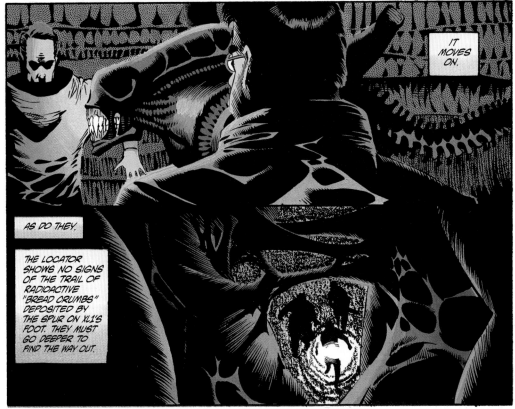

IT
MOVES
ON.

AS DO THEY.

THE LOCATOR
SHOWS NO SIGNS
OF THE TRAIL OF
RADIOACTIVE
"BREAD CRUMBS"
DEPOSITED BY
THE SPUR ON XL1'S
FOOT. THEY MUST
GO DEEPER TO
FIND THE WAY OUT.

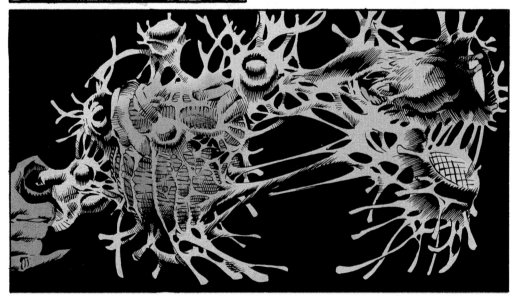

When asked why an ant needed to be equipped with a miniaturized cold plasma laser, Mayakovsky answered: "I'd want one."

From *Cyberantics* by Stanislaw Mayakovsky.

HURRY, STAN!

GO! GO! DON'T SLOW DOWN FOR ME!

HOBAN, DO YOU COPY?

GILL, PLEASE LET HER REST.

Uh, I...

IT LOOKS LIKE I TRIPPED A FEW CIRCUITS TOO MANY.

DR. MAYAKOVSKY, I...

IT'S ALL RIGHT. SHE MAKES ME FEEL THAT WAY, TOO.

LET'S SEE HOW OUR GUESTS ARE DOING.

"HERE THEY COME.

"GILL, THAT IS THE APERTURE THROUGH THE FIELD. DO YOU SEE IT?

"CLASSIC STRATEGY. POTTER DIDN'T ANTICIPATE THEIR CLEVERNESS.

" HAVE YOU EVER SEEN ANYTHING MOVE SO QUICKLY?

"THEY'LL NEVER EVEN KNOW WHAT HIT THEM.

"I WOULD HATE TO ENCOUNTER THE **PREDATOR** THAT ACID DEFENSE WAS EVOLVED TO THWART."

IT'S OVER QUICKLY FOR MOST.

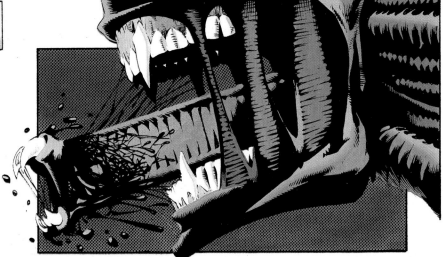

BUT SOME OF THEM AREN'T SO LUCKY.

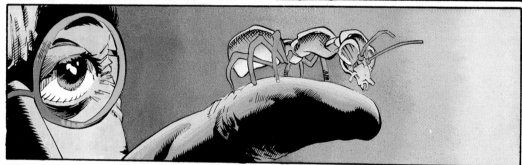

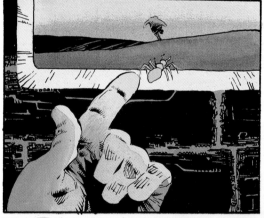

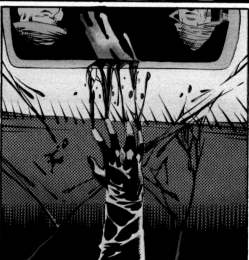

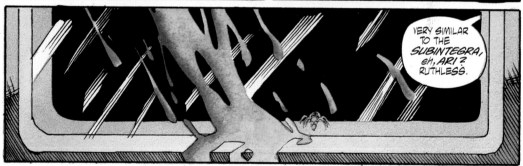

VERY SIMILAR TO THE *SUBINTEGRA*, eh, *ARI 2* RUTHLESS.

DON'T LOOK, IF IT UPSETS YOU.

MAYAKOVSKY! GOD*DAMN* IT! THOSE THINGS ARE KILLING MY MEN!

IT LOOKS LIKE THE CAPTAIN'S ANGRY. I THINK HE FINALLY SEES THE IRONY OF OUR SITUATION.

YES, CAPTAIN, I'VE BEEN EXPECTING YOUR CALL.

WE HAVE SOME PRESSING ISSUES THAT WE NEED TO DISCUSS. I HAVE A PLAN.

I HAVE A FEELING I WON'T BE SEEING YOU AGAIN.

YEAH, HE'S A
SYNTH ALL RIGHT.

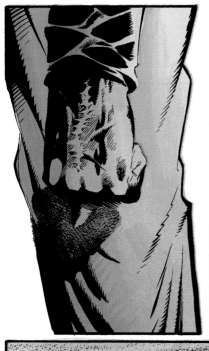

INSIDE.

THIS IS GETTING WEIRD. NOTIFY THE CAPTAIN.

SUS, I'M
EEZING.

WE'LL GET OUT OF THIS.

I'M SURE WE WILL, STAN. ONE WAY OR ANOTHER.

STOP LOOKING AT ME LIKE THAT. I'M FINE. WE'VE GOT IT ALL. DON'T WORRY.

DR. MAYAKOVSKY? I HAVE REACHED THE LANCET.

CAPTAIN POTTER DOES NOT FEEL THE NEED TO NEGOTIATE.

IN FACT, IT IS ONLY THE PRESENCE OF THE COLLECTED JELLY THAT KEEPS HIM FROM DESTROYING THE SHIP AND YOU ALONG WITH IT.

BZZZZZZ

POTTER, I THINK YOU SHOULD BE PREPARED TO GO HOME EMPTY-HANDED.

DON'T THREATEN ME.

NO, CAPTAIN, DON'T THREATEN *ME*. YOU HAVE TWENTY MINUTES TO LIFT OFF THE PLANET'S SURFACE.

YOU MUST BE JOKING. DO YOU REALLY THINK I'M GOING TO LET YOU LEAVE WITH ANY OF THIS CARGO?

WE'LL SEE. GOOD-BYE.

HAVE ANY IDEAS?

NEITHER DO I. I THINK GILL WILL HAVE TO TAKE CARE OF THINGS ON HIS END.

HOBAN--

CHRIST, STAN! YOU DON'T KNOW WHAT I HAD TO DO TO AVOID DETECTION. NOW YOU JUST *GAVE AWAY* MY POSITION?

SHUT UP! I'M GOING TO BE DUSTING OFF IN ABOUT TWENTY-FIVE MINUTES, IF I CAN GET TO THE COCKPIT. IF I DON'T GET OFF THE GROUND BY THEN, SEND A LANDER.

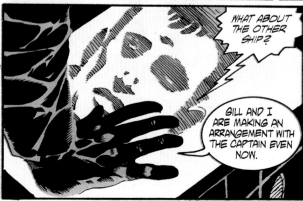

WHAT ABOUT THE OTHER SHIP?

GILL AND I ARE MAKING AN ARRANGEMENT WITH THE CAPTAIN EVEN NOW.

I'LL SEE YOU SOON.

I HOPE SO.

I WANT YOU TO REMEMBER THIS, ARI, IN CASE WE DON'T MAKE IT OUT OF HERE.

DON'T WORRY ABOUT ME. I...WE HAVE SOMEPLACE SAFE TO GO.

DON'T LOOK AT ME LIKE THAT. I KNOW SHE'S NOT GOING TO MAKE IT.

THINK OF ME WHENEVER YOU ACCESS THIS FILE, AND DON'T BE LONELY...

...WE WON'T.

I'M TIRED OF THIS SHIT. I'M GOING TO RAISE LANCET AND REPOSITION SO I CAN THROW THE PERIMETER FIELD AROUND THE HARVESTER.

YOU HAD BETTER BE *CONVINCING.* ACTIVATE AUDIO.

THE CAPTAIN WILL NOT AGREE TO YOUR TERMS. IN FACT, HE HAS A PLAN WHICH WILL RESULT IN THEIR TAKING THE SHIP.

THEN IT SEEMS WE NO LONGER HAVE ANYTHING TO TALK ABOUT.

GOOD-BYE, CAPTAIN POTTER.

THANK YOU, GILL. IT'S BEEN A PLEASURE.

ACTIVATE SUBROUTINE *DIOGENES.*

GENTLEMEN, IN THE RICH MAN'S HOUSE...

CRICK

CRAK

...THERE IS NO PLACE TO SPIT...

...BUT IN HIS FACE.

SNAP

BAHWHOOOM

BOOM BOOM BOOM

WHAT.. WAS THAT? I... I'M HAVING TROUBLE BREATHING... STAN...

I THINK OUR FRIENDS AT THE DOOR ARE BECOMING AGITATED. THEY SENSE THE CHEMICAL CHANGES FROM THE CREATURES OUTSIDE.

HOBAN'S ON HIS WAY, BUT WE'RE RUNNING OUT OF TIME.

WHEN HE GETS HERE, HE CAN HAVE IT ALL. I DON'T CARE ANYMORE.

I'M SORRY, JULIE. THIS WASN'T HOW THINGS WERE SUPPOSED TO BE.

BUT THERE'S STILL A PLACE WE CAN GO... TOGETHER THIS TIME.

IS THIS THE PLACE YOU WANTED TO REACH THE WHOLE TIME? TO GO INSIDE AND NEVER COME OUT?

IT'S OKAY. TAKE ME WITH YOU. I'M READY.

I'LL REMEMBER YOU THIS WAY ...FOREVER.

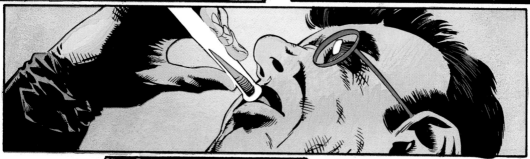

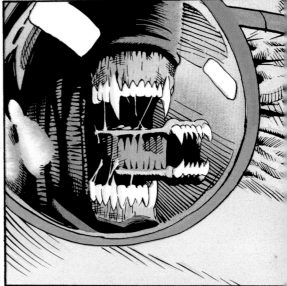
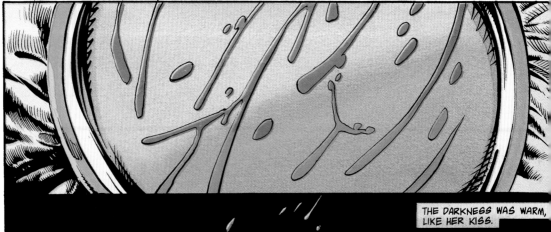

THE DARKNESS WAS WARM, LIKE HER KISS.

STAN COULDN'T TELL IF HIS
EYES WERE OPENED OR CLOSED.

HE REMEMBERED SOMETHING BY
OTA DOKAN, A JAPANESE POET—
WRITTEN WHILE A KNIFE PROTRUDED
FROM HIS CHEST.

"HAD I NOT KNOWN THAT I WAS DEAD

ALREADY...

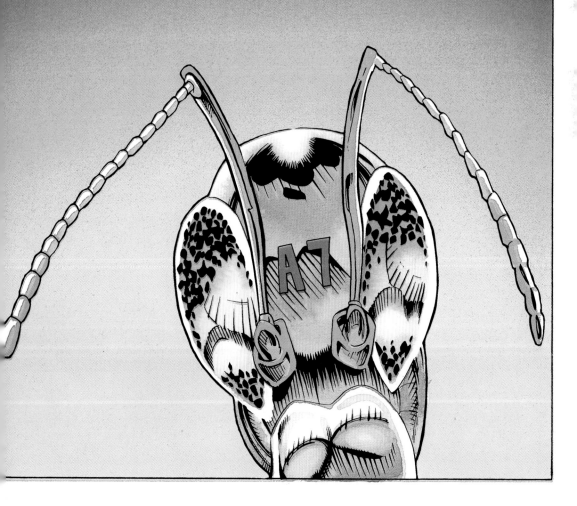

"I WOULD HAVE MOURNED...

"...THE LOSS...

"...OF MY LIFE."

ALIENS™

Biographies

Jerry Prosser, a professional comics writer, is the author of *Exquisite Corpse* and *Cyberantics*. He has a master's degree in social work and worked for a number of years as an editor and editorial coordinator at Dark Horse Comics.

The category is Comic-Book Artist. Remember to answer in the form of a question. This artist first gained attention for his revisionist versions of DC Comics' *Deadman* and *Sandman* as well as a series of successful *Batman* graphic novels. He gained infamy for giving Batman really long ears on the monthly *Batman* title, and the sacrilege lasted three years. He also drew *Venom, The Madness,* and a *Magneto* miniseries for Marvel. His eccentric nature was publicly exposed with his creator-owned title, *The Hammer,* for the intrepid publishing company Dark Horse Comics. Who is Kelley Jones?

Les Dorscheid began painting products. Food, mostly: cheese, salad dressing, crackers, and something called Flavor Fry. In the early '80s, Richard Bruning gave Les a shot at color painting comics. Since then, Les has worked on dozens of titles, including *Deadman* and *Batman: Red Rain.* Les' most recent comics work was with Kelley Jones on *The Hammer.* In addition to comic-book, trade-paperback cover, and gaming-product freelance work, Les designs computer games such as "Hexen2," "Mageslayer," and "Take No Prisoners" for Raven Software.

John Bolton spends far too much time painting in his eerie, prop-filled studio in North London. An award-winning artist who has worked on books with Chris Claremont, Neil Gaiman, Clive Barker, Sam Raimi, Anne Rice, and many others, and whose ethereal vampire-women and magical creatures have made his work much sought after, John has handled assignments for every major publisher in the comics field. His interest in the stylishly bizarre is evidenced throughout his work, and he currently has his own international fan club and magazine.

ALIENS™
HARVEST
G A L L E R Y

Artist Kelley Jones was afraid of Aliens until he drew them for Dark Horse! Below is a piece he did for the January 1992 Dark Horse *Insider* back cover. The four covers to the *Aliens: Hive* comic-book series follow, including the original line art for issues #1 and #2 and an unused cover.

ALIENS

FEMALE WAR
(formerly *Aliens: Earth War*)
Verheiden • Kieth
112-page color paperback
ISBN: 1-85286-784-1 £11.99

GENOCIDE
Arcudi • Willis • Story
112-page color paperback
ISBN: 1-85286-805-8 £10.99

LABYRINTH
Woodring • Plunkett
136-page color paperback
ISBN: 1-85286-844-9 £11.99

NIGHTMARE ASYLUM
(formerly *Aliens: Book Two*)
Verheiden • Beauvais
112-page color paperback
ISBN: 1-85286-765-5 £11.99

NEWT'S TALE
Richardson • Somerville • Garvey
96-page color paperback
ISBN: 1-85286-575-x £6.99

ROGUE
Edginton • Simpson
112-page color paperback
ISBN: 1-85286-838-4 £11.99

OUTBREAK
(formerly *Aliens: Book One*)
Verheiden • Nelson
168-page B&W paperback
ISBN: 1-85286-756-6 £11.99

STRONGHOLD
Arcudi • Mahnke • Palmiotti
112-page color paperback
ISBN: 1-85286-875-9 £11.99

ALIENS VS PREDATOR

ALIENS VS PREDATOR
Stradley • Warner
176-page color paperback
ISBN: 1-85286-413-3 £10.99

WAR
Stradley • Warner
200-page color paperback
ISBN: 1-85286-703-5 £12.99

PREDATOR

PREDATOR
Verheiden • Warner • Randall
168-page color paperback
ISBN: 1-85286-377-3 £7.50

BIG GAME
Arcudi • Dorkin • Gil
112-page color paperback
ISBN: 1-85286-454-0 £7.50

COLD WAR
Verheiden • Randall • Mitchell
112-page color paperback
ISBN: 1-85286-576-8 £8.99

All *Aliens* and *Predator* publications are available through most good bookshops or direct from our mail order service at Titan Books. For a free graphic novels catalogue or to order, telephone 01536 763 631 with your credit card details or contact Titan Books Mail Order PO Box 54, Desborough, Northants., NN14 2UH, quoting reference AHARVEST/GN.